Santa & Co

SANTA & CO

Jamie Charteris

Michael O'Mara Books Limited

First published in Great Britain in 1999
by Michael O'Mara Books Limited
9 Lion Yard
Tremadoc Road
London SW4 7NQ

Santa & Co is published under licence from Paperlink Ltd
356 Kennington Road, London SE11 4LD.
Copyright © Paperlink Ltd 1999.

A CIP catalogue record for this book is available from
the British Library

ISBN 1-85479-455-8

1 3 5 7 9 10 8 6 4 2

Designed by Mick Keates
Formatting by Concise Artisans
Printed and bound in Great Britain by
Cox & Wyman Ltd, Reading, Berks.

5

6

8

9

11

13

14

22

23

29

34

37

41

42

43

45

47

52

55

60

63

71

75

76

78

83

91